# Candle Snuffers

by

Martin Fry Wolton

Willowbeck Publications

A CIP catalogue record for this book is available from the British Library.

© Martin Fry Wolton 2000

ISBN 0 9537545 0 2

Typeset and printed by
*The Lowfield Printing Company, Dartford, Kent*

Published by
WILLOWBECK PUBLICATIONS,
Willowbeck House,
Station Road,
Pulham St. Mary,
Diss,
Norfolk IP21 4QS
e-mail: willowbeckpubs@cs.com

Colour Photographs (cover pages):
Napthens Photography, Harleston, Norfolk

Black and white photographs (pages 14 to 53)
by the Author

Dedicated to my dear wife

JOY MARGARET

# PREFACE

When I first began collecting candle snuffers, I found little information on them, and certainly few detailed descriptions. I was also at a loss to know what was a fair price to pay for them. So I feel that this book will not only help collectors by describing the various types but will also help with valuations. Snuffers can be purchased from £15 upwards, and can be ideal antiques for the new collector.

I have been encouraged to produce this book by antique dealers, who have told me that there is little specialised information published solely in this field. I have been helped in the preparation of this book by, in particular, Mr M. H. E Horner, B.A.D.A.Dip., antiquarian Horologist, who also specialises in early weapons and metalware and by Mrs Barbara Winter-Hodges of Antelope Antiques. I would also like to record my appreciation of the very considerable help given by Mr Len Hudson in the preparation of this book.

Further suggested reading is the comprehensive book *"Making Fire and Light in the Home pre-1820"* by John Caspall, published in 1987 and reprinted in 1992 and 1995 by the Antique Collectors Club.

*Martin Fry Wolton*
Diss, Norfolk.
July 2000

# GLOSSARY

**Britannia metal, or white metal**
Alloy of tin, antimony and copper, more serviceable than pewter.

**Candlesheres or Candlesheares**
Earliest crude scissor snuffers made of wrought iron. Also called wick trimmers (see p. 7).

(see p. 7)

**Chamberstick**
Also called a bedroom candlestick. A type of small, portable candlestick set on a plate-shaped base with a small handle, some examples having a tapered slot in the base of the candle socket, especially designed to hold tapered snuffers.

**Close-plate**
A technique of hand plating by using tin to solder silver foil onto steel or brass, in use from the 18th century until the early 20th century. Candle snuffers which have been close-plated can often be identified by observing a seam on the inside of their handles.

**Dousing cones**
Conical extinguishers.

**Douter**
Article with scissor-like action, for extinguishing flame by nipping - 'do out' or 'out quencher'. Sometimes forming part of a candle snuffer.

**Eccentric action**
Ingenious mechanical device for trapping snuff in snuffer box.

**Electro plating**
Silver deposited on base metal. From c.1840 began to supersede Old Sheffield Plate, which, however, continued to be made in small quantities until c.1920.

| | |
|---|---|
| Fence snuffers | Simple snuffers with fence around on one edge. |
| Go-to bed | Very small handleless Chambersticks (see p. 5). |
| Hobday snuffers | Snuffers having a springless action for retaining snuff in box. |
| Japanning | The application of laquer, a type of varnish, to the surface of a material. |
| Nickel-silver | Alloy containing no silver, but of copper, nickel and zinc, date c.1825. Argentan, Pakton, Tutenag and German Silver are variations of this alloy. Articles made of nickel-silver were quite commonly electro-plated from 1840 onwards. |
| Old Sheffield Plate | Silver, fused on copper. Trays (and, rarely, snuffers) were directly made from this fused material from 1742 until they were no longer in demand. |
| Papier Maché | Pulped paper glued and pressed. Used for trays. |
| Pewter | Latterly, mainly an alloy of tin and copper. |
| Podkin (archaic) | Dousing cone being part of a candle set of chamber candlesticks, with snuffer in slot in stem and podkin. |
| Snuff | Burnt wick. |

| | |
|---|---|
| Toleware | Thin metal decorated by painting. |
| Treen | Made from wood. Examples of trays in olivewood and walnut are known. |
| Wick trimmers | Candlesheares (see p. 5). Later variants had a fence bordering the lower blade and sometimes this blade was fitted in a dish to hold the hot snuff. |

# INTRODUCTION

The wick in old types of candle was usually made of a material, such as twisted fibres, that either burnt quickly and charred, or burnt slowly and gradually drooped into the melted wax. The burnt wick (or snuff) had therefore to be cut frequently to avoid mess and guttering.

So snuffers were invented to remove the snuff. The word "snuffers" is sometimes, confusingly, applied to conical extinguishers, also known as dousing cones, which may still be found in ecclesiastical and occasionally, domestic use. Actual snuffers were made from about the middle of the fifteenth century until the end of the nineteenth century, after which the improvements which took place in both candles and their wicks made them increasingly redundant. Such later, improved, wicks were made of plaited cotton which burnt in a satisfactory manner. However, some inferior candles were still made and used, because of their cheapness, and snuffers were, therefore, still present in the home beyond the end of the nineteenth century.

The earliest snuffers were called Candlesheres or Candlesheares and were wick trimmers (scissors) made of crude wrought iron. Later other, more valuable, metals were used, and the word snuffer came to be applied. The British Museum has on display a pair of snuffers made of silver with two oval medallions, gold and enamelled, and depicting the arms of Henry VIII and of Cardinal Bainbridge, who died in 1514; these are reputedly the earliest English snuffers of this type still in existence.

Snuffers were of scissor action, invariably having a point at the end to lift the wick to prepare it for cutting. A pair of snuffers (otherwise called snuffers in the same manner as a pair of scissors is called scissors) would commonly be one of the following types.

1. Early rare heart shaped snuffers with a box on each blade  as depicted in Figs. 57 and 63.

2. Fence snuffers, which are simple wick trimmers. These do not have a box, but rather a narrow "fence" around one blade to prevent the snuff from falling off, as shown in Fig 52.

3.  Snuffers with one of the pivoted blades having a box with a cutting edge, and with the other blade having a cutting edge only. This latter blade, after cutting the wick, usually pushed the wick (or snuff) into the rear of the box on the other blade, thus pressing it to make sure it was extinguished.

Some snuffers also had Douters (from the words "do out") to extinguish the flame by nipping (or pressing) it before the snuff was removed. Examples of these are to be seen in Figs. 9 and 22. Examples of Douters alone are seen in Figs. 33 to 37 inclusive, and Fig. 64.

Snuffers contained the snuff until the next time they were used. Then, unfortunately, the old snuff might fall out so various ingenious methods were used (in snuffers of category 3 above) to retain the  burnt wick until emptying was required. The most commonly used of this type is the "eccentric action" snuffer, such as is illustrated in Fig. 8.

The eccentric action is so called because a crank or eccentric pin in the handle pivot assembly operates a long thin bar along the base of the snuffer, which engages with a linkage to the vertical blade which is in a slot along the axis of the box. Opening the scissor action "cocks"  the mechanism, and then on closing the handles the wick is cut by the side blade. At the same time the vertical blade rises, enabling the snuff to be pushed under it by the side blade into the opposite side of the box. The vertical blade then falls by a snap action thus trapping the snuff even when the scissor action is later fully opened. One can either use the snuffers again, if there is not too much snuff in the box, or, by raising the vertical blade by hand and opening the scissor action, empty the box by shaking the snuff out.

Some eccentric action snuffers, such as illustrated in Fig. 39, have a sprung side plate which can be lifted up by hand for the snuff to be removed. This does not entail opening the scissor action. There is no pressing (or nipping) extinguishing effect with the eccentric action type, which commonly do not have Douters as part of their mechanism, but of course the burnt wick is securely contained.

Another type (among many mechanical snuffers) is the Hobday patent snuffer. There are no springs in this particular type of snuffer. Opening the snuffers lifts, by an inclined plane action, the wick side of the box so enabling the cut wick to enter the box. Then the box side closes. There is no extinguishing action.

Additionally, there are various types of snuffers with ingenious mechanical actions such as those which enable the snuff to be emptied out without opening the scissor action, see Figs. 25, 26, 28, 29, 30, 31, 39, 42 and 76. There are also those which have no springs at all, not even in the pivot joint. For examples of these see (i) the Hobday type (as referred to above) in Figs. 12, 13, 15, 17 and 19; (ii) the eccentric action type in Figs. 14, 16, 20 and 24; (iii) the cylinder type in Fig. 32; and (iv) the trapdoor type shown in Fig. 49. Another unusual device is illustrated in Fig. 27.

It was not usual for snuffers and snuffers trays to be made as a set, because trays were often made by candlestick makers, and snuffers by specialist manufacturers. However, there were exceptions to this rule, as shown in Figs. 1, 41, 58 and 71, where the snuffers and trays are made by the same manufacturers. Some mechanical snuffers were made by manufacturers who also made steel toys.

### Snuffers were made of a great variety of materials, viz:

Wrought iron, which was often Japanned
Cast iron
Wrought steel
Brass
Nickel-silver
Close-plated silver foil on steel
Electroplate (e.g. on copper-plated steel or nickel-silver)
Old Sheffield Plate (sandwich of fused copper and silver)

### Trays were generally made of:

Toleware
Papier-maché
Pewter
Sheet brass
Cast brass
Silver
Close-plated silver
Old Sheffield Plate
Nickel-silver, sometimes electroplated
Treen (wood) e.g. Olive wood, Walnut – only rarely used and therefore very uncommon.

For an explanation of those terms which may not be im-
mediately familiar to the reader, please see the Glossary on pages 5, 6 and 7.

Trays often followed the same pattern and shape irrespective of the material of which they were made. For example, the writer has seen the trays in Figs. 54 and 55 both in Toleware and in Papier-Maché; and the tray in Fig. 56 both in Papier-Maché and in Old Sheffield Plate.

Electroplating was introduced in the mid nineteenth century. To be more exact, both Elkington and Co., Birmingham, and John Stephen Woolrich took out patents in 1840. The new method came into general use sufficiently widely to be listed under a separate directory entry "Electro platers" in the 1849 Sheffield Directory. By the mid 1850's it had forced all the manufacturers of Old Sheffield Plate out of business, and it continued to dominate the market throughout the rest of the century.

## Order of illustrations

A note of explanation of the order in which I have placed the illustrations may be helpful to the reader.

In general, the illustrations begin with the less valuable materials such as iron and steel, then progressing to the most valuable of all – silver. So Figs. 1 to 53 show snuffers and douters mainly made of iron, steel, close-plated steel and nickel-silver. Thereafter, Figs. 54-56 show trays made of Toleware or Papier-Maché; Figs. 57-69 show snuffers and a douter made of brass; Figs. 70 and 71 show a candlestick and snuffer made of Old Sheffield Plate; Figs. 72-78 show additional snuffers made of steel basically, including those with silver handles; Figs. 79-86 show snuffers and trays made mainly (but not exclusively) of Silver. Figs. 3, 21 22, 47 and 48 show tapered snuffers specially made to fit into Chambersticks (see Glossary); Fig. 70 shows a Chamberstick with snuffers and dousing cone. Figs. 62, 63 and 64 show the most recent additions that were added to my own collection.

I have held in my collection all the snuffers illustrated in this book. The prices given are based on those I paid over a number of years as the collection was being assembled, *adjusted to curent market levels*. However, it must be pointed out that candle snuffers, like other antiques, may become available at a wide range of prices depending on the source of supply and the circumstances of the sale. My collection does not include any snuffers in silver earlier than the eighteenth century; a silver snuffer and tray set prior to that could, in good condition, be worth considerably more than any of those illustrated in this book. When dealing with antiques pin-point accuracy as to prices is simply not possible.

**Fig. 1**

Snuffers with tray and two extinguishers, one being shown away from its cone mount.
Iron. Total length 17cm
Japanned
Rare.　　　　　　　　　　Date c.1820　　　　　　　　Value £70


**Fig. 2**

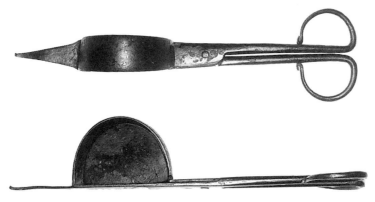

Wrought Iron Snuffers. 21cm
Japanned
Uncommon　　　　　　　　Date c.1720　　　　　　　　Value £80

*Fig. 3*

Tapered snuffers
Iron.  14cm
Common                    Date c.1800                    Value £20

*Fig. 4*

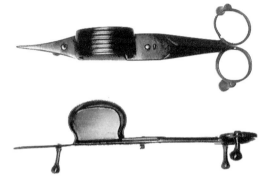

Snuffers
Steel.  16.5cm
Common                    Date c.1790                    Value £30

*Fig. 5*

Egg-shaped snuffers
Steel.  16.5cm
Rare                      Date c.1830                    Value £120

**Fig. 6**

Snuffers with facetted top. 'VR - Brookes'
Steel.  17cm
Uncommon                    Date c.1840                    Value £60


**Fig. 7**
**Top, bottom and side**
**views**

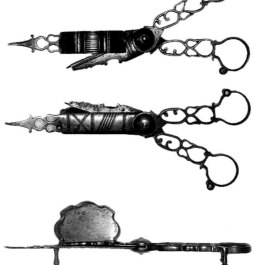

Fine decorative snuffers
Iron.  18cm
English
Very rare.               Date c.1780-1790               Value £190

16

**Fig. 8**

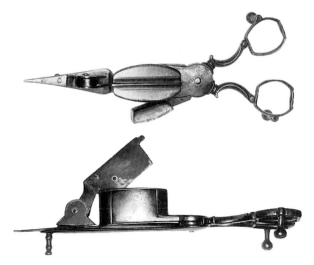

Oval snuffers.
Eccentric operated blade for retaining snuff.
Steel.  19cm
Rare                    Date c.1830                    Value £160

**Fig. 9**

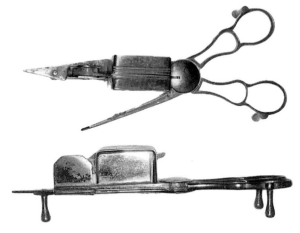

Snuffer and Douter.
Eccentric operated blade for retaining snuff.
Steel.  17cm
Rare                    Date 1800-1830                    Value £125

**Fig. 10**

Eccentric operated blade snuffer for retaining snuff.
'WR - Brookes'. Steel. 17cm
Rare                              Date 1830-1837                    Value £75


**Fig. 11**

Eccentric operated blade for retaining snuff.
'Rove & Co Patent'. Steel. 18cm
Common                        Date c.1820                       Value £55


**Fig. 12**

Snuffers of Hobday type.
'Improved Patent Lever without Springs'.
Close-plated. 17cm
Uncommon                    Date 1810-1820                  Value £50

*Fig. 13*

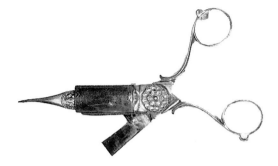

'Hobday Royal Letters Patent'.
Close-plated with silver mounts.  17cm
Uncommon                    Date c.1825                    Value £65


*Fig. 14*

Snuffers eccentric action.
On blade 'Cope & Cutler Patent Lever Without Springs'.
On boss 'Cope & Cutler by His Majesty's Royal Letters Patent'.
Steel - Close-plated.  16cm
Rare                    Date 1820-1837                    Value £65

*Fig. 15*

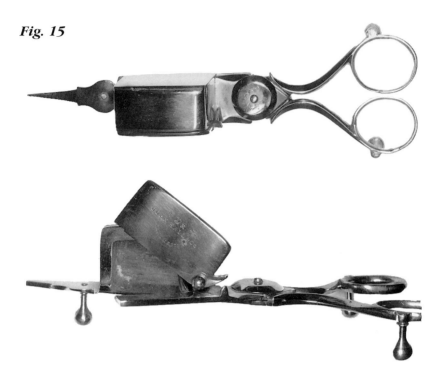

Hobday type.
The close-up photograph shows the Inclined Plane action.
'VR - John Hall & Co., Manchester'.
Steel.  18cm
Uncommon               Date c.1840               Value £60

*Fig. 16*

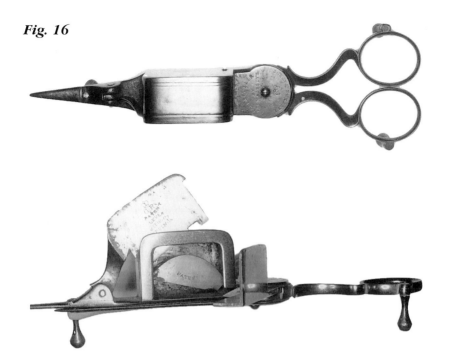

Snuffer eccentric operated.
On blade 'GR Patent Lever without Springs'.
On inside face of blade there are two dots.
On boss 'Cope & Cutler by His Majesty's Letters Patent'.
On snuff retainer inside 'Patent'. See close-up.
Steel.  17.5cm
Very rare                     Date 1820-1830                    Value £150

**Fig. 17**

Hobday Snuffers.
'Royal Letters Patent Hobday & Co'.
On back of blade four triangles.
Deep belly and big pad feet.
Steel.  17cm
Uncommon                    Date c.1820                    Value £60

**Fig. 18**

Hobday type.
On blade Fleur de Lys and 'Improved Lever'.
On boss 'By His Majesty's Letters Patent'.
Handle spring.
Steel.  17.5cm
Uncommon                    Date c.1820                    Value £60

**Fig. 19**

Hobday snuffer.
On blade 'Hobday & Co Patent'.
Steel.  16.5cm
Uncommon                    Date c.1820                    Value £50

**Fig. 20**

Eccentric operated snuffer.
On blade 'WR - Patent Lever without Springs'.
On boss 'Lund by His Majesty's Letters Patent'.
Steel.  17.5cm
Rare                         Date 1830-1837                    Value £100


**Fig. 21**

Chamberstick tapered snuffers.
Steel.  13.5cm
Common                       Date Early 19th cent.             Value £25

**Fig. 22**

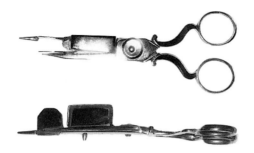

Chamberstick tapered snuffers with douter.
Steel.  13.5cm
Rare                    Date c.1880                    Value £80

**Fig. 23**

Unusually small snuffers by 'MORTON'.
Steel.  9cm
Rare            Late 18th to early 19th cent.            Value £75

**Fig. 24**

Eccentric by 'Gilbert By His Majesty's Letters Patent'.
On blade 'WR Patent Lever without Springs'.
Steel with close-plated handles and lead-filled silver mounts.
18cm
Uncommon              Date 1830-1837              Value £100

**Fig. 25**

'HNS Shrapnel VR Patent'. 'Manufactured by T Cutler, Birmingham'.
Steel with close-plated handles and lead-filled silver mounts. 17cm Box lid has pins for retaining snuff, as shown. Note that Shrapnel's full name is Henry Needham Scrope Shrapnel.
Rare                        Date c.1840                        Value £120

**Fig. 26**

'HNS Shrapnel Patent VR'. 'Rodgers & Sons Sheffield'.
Steel. Box has hinged side with pins for retaining snuff.   17cm See lower illustration.
Rare                        Date c.1840                        Value £120

*Fig. 27*

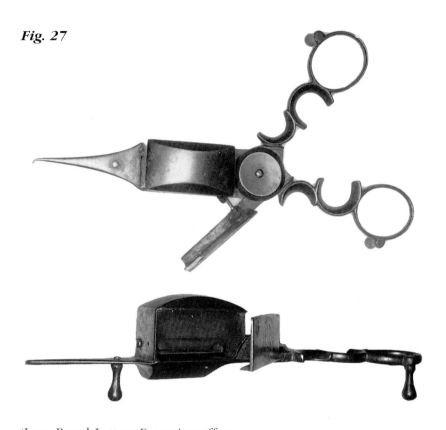

'Lees Royal Letters Patent' snuffer.
Inclined plane with internal opening sprung trapdoor.
Steel.  17cm
Very rare.                    Date c.1820                    Value £100

**Fig. 28**

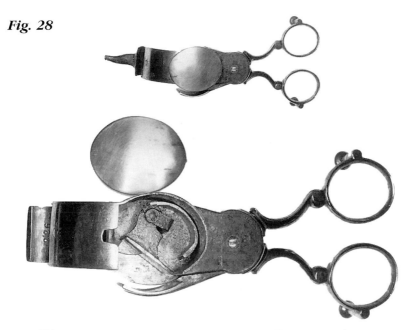

'J Duff by His Majesty's Letters Patent' Snuffer No. 226.
Ingenious action for shooting snuff into front compartment which
hinges down for emptying.
Steel. 16.5cm
Very rare.                    Date c.1810                    Value £150

**Fig. 29**

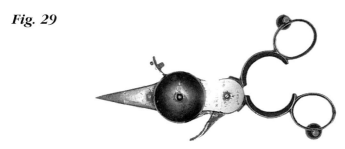

Snuffer by Bright & Sons. Large ball feet.
Ingenious snap spring action for trapping snuff which then emp-
tied by opening side door.
Steel. 15cm
Very rare.                    Date c.1810                    Value £150

**Fig. 30**

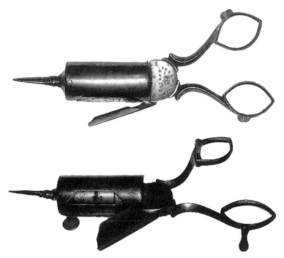

Cylindrical snuffer patented by Willmores.
Revolving internal curved trapdoor which is closed by a snap
spring action.
Steel. 16cm
Rare.                      Date c.1812                    Value £150

**Fig. 31**

'Cope & Cutler Patent' snuffer.
Sliding trapdoor in base 'Improved Slide'. Rear feet act as handle
for slide emptying snuff.
Steel.  17.5cm
Rare.                      Date c.1820                    Value £100

**Fig. 32**

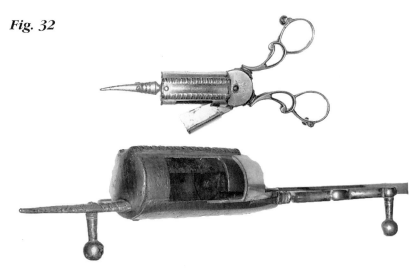

Snuffer by 'Saml Armfield' 'Lever Patent'.
Revolving curved trapdoor. Made with no springs.
Close-plated.  17cm
Rare.                    Date c.1800                    Value £120

**Fig. 33**

Douter.
Steel.  11.5cm
Rare.                    Date c.1800                    Value £60

**Fig. 34**

Douter. No legs.
Steel. 10.5cm
Rare                    Date c.1800                    Value £60

*Fig. 35*

Douter with wick lifter.
Steel.   13cm
Rare.                    Date c.1780                    Value £60


*Fig. 36*

Douter with three legs.
Close-plated.   11cm
Rare.                    Date c.1800                    Value £60


*Fig. 37*

Douter. Eastern.
Bronze.   11.5cm
Rare.                    Date c.1800                    Value £80

**Fig. 38**

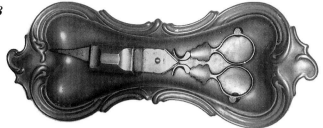

Snuffers. Tinned iron for pewter finish. 17cm
Uncommon.             Date c.1800-1820           Value £45
On tray by Broadhead & Atkin, Sheffield. Pewter. 26cm
Common.                Date c.1840             Value £40

**Fig. 39**

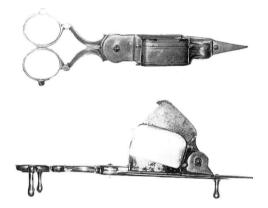

Eccentric snuffer. On blade 'The Springs warranted'.
Also has sprung side plate for emptying. Close-plated.  18cm
Rare.                   Date c.1820           Value £125

**Fig. 40**

Snuffers. Close-plated with silver boss.  18cm
Common.               Date c.1810             Value £80

**Fig. 41**

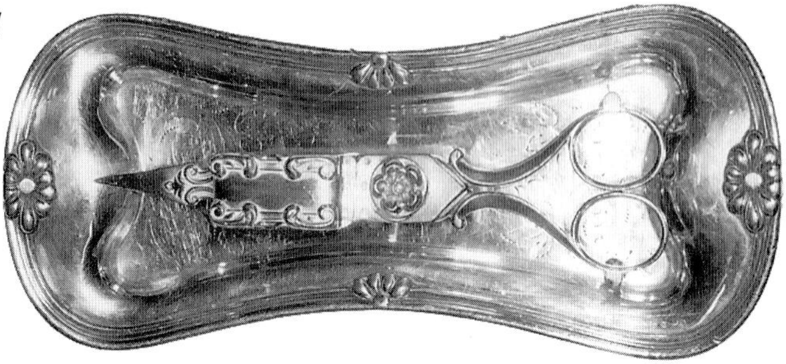

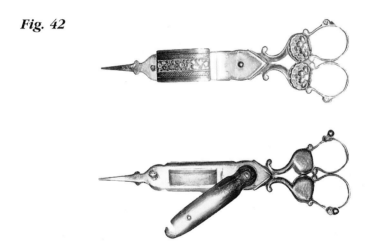

Snuffers 'Prime'.
Close-plated with lead-filled silver mounts.  16.5cm
Common.                    Date c.1840                    Value £50
On tray 'Prime'.
Old Sheffield Plate.  22.5cm
Rare.                    Date c.1800                    Value £60
NB. It is very rare to find snuffers/tray by the same manufacturer.


**Fig. 42**

Snuffers with trap-door in base.
Copper/silver fused thin sheet, close-plated on iron.  18cm
Rare.                    Date c.1810                    Value £100

**Fig. 43**

Snuffers.
Close-plated.   17.5cm
Common.                    Date c.1810                    Value £50

**Fig. 44**

Very good quality (?ecclesiastical) snuffers.
Nickel Silver with silver boss and makers marks.   17.5cm
Rare.                      Date c.1825                    Value £100

**Fig. 45**

Snuffers with makers marks.
Nickel Silver.   17.5cm
Uncommon.                  Date c.1850                    Value £60

**Fig. 46**

Snuffers with makers marks (?Birmingham).
Nickel Silver.   18cm
Uncommon.                  Date c.1825                    Value £45

**Fig. 47**

Chamberstick tapered snuffers with makers marks.
Nickel Silver.  13cm
Uncommon.                    Date c.1825                    Value £40

**Fig. 48**

Chamberstick tapered snuffers,
Steel with close-plated handles.  14.5cm
Uncommon.                    Date c.1830                    Value £55

**Fig. 49**

'Haigh & Co Patent' snuffers.
Trapdoor falls over deep floor when snuffers closed.
Nickel Silver. Part of handles missing.  Estimated 18cm
Rare.                         Date c.1825                    Value £95

**Fig. 50**

Wick-trimmer of cast iron. 'Patent Oct 4 81'.
On closing brush sweeps snuff into lower compartment.  14cm
Very rare.                    Date c.1881                    Value £75

**Fig. 51**

Wick-trimmer (fence missing).
Steel.  15cm
Uncommon.                 Date 19th cent.                         Value £20


**Fig. 52**

Wick-trimmer with fence. 'JAH & Co'.
Steel.  15.5cm
Common.                   Date 19th cent.                         Value £30


**Fig. 53**

Wick-trimmer. 'Bromley's Night Lamp'.
Steel. 'Tomlinson & Son, Sheffield'.  10cm
Rare.                     Date 19th cent.                         Value £40

**Fig. 54**

Snuffer Tray.
Pearl inlaid Toleware.   26cm
Rare.                           Date 1800-1850                    Value £90


**Fig. 55**

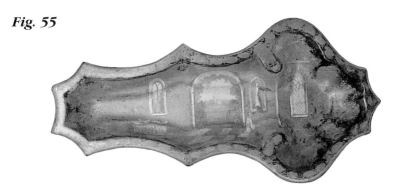

Snuffer Tray.
Papier-maché.   24cm
Uncommon.          Date Early 19th cent.                Value £80

**Fig. 56**

Snuffer Tray.
Papier-maché.  26cm
Uncommon.           Date Early 19th cent.              Value £80


**Fig. 57**

A pair of very old exquisite snuffers.
Manufacturer's mark on base.
Box on each blade.
Continental.  Length 20cm
Brass.
Very rare.              Date c.1650                     Value £425

**Fig. 58**

A pair of early snuffers and tray.
The snuffers have a crowned 'G' on top of left handle.
English. Length 17cm
The tray has three ball feet and finger loop.
The set is brass.  27cm
Very rare.                    Date 1700-1720                    Value £425


**Fig. 59**

Pair of good quality snuffers 16cm with swan design handles on heavy cast tray.
The set is Brass.  23cm
Uncommon.                    Date 1790-1810                    Value £100

*Fig. 60*

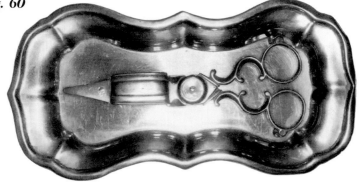

Pair of snuffers 16cm on tray.
Brass.  23.5cm
Common.              Date c.1790              Value £60

*Fig. 61*

Two pairs of small snuffers.
11cm long with grooved snipe noses.
Sometimes attached by chains to Eastern European lamps and
candle stands.
Brass.
Rare.              Date c.1810              Value £60 each

**Fig. 62**

Snuffers on tray with feet. English.
Brass. Snuffers 16.5cm. Tray 18.5cm
Very rare.              Date 1st quarter 18th c.              Value £375

**Fig. 63**

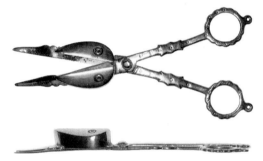

Fine snuffers – symetrical with box on each blade.
Brass. Length 16cm. Continental.
Very rare.              Date c.1700              Value £250

**Fig. 64**

Douters. English.
Brass. 11cm
Rare.              Date c.1780              Value £60

**Fig. 65**

Two sets of snuffers.  14cm
Housed in vertical stands.  10.5cm
These are apparently reproductions, which have a rough surface
inside the holders.
Cast Brass.
Uncommon.   Original Date George II c.1750   Value £180 per set.
N.B. A very rare original set could be estimated to have a value
of at least £500.

**Fig. 66**

Pair of heavy turned candlesticks. 17.5cm
One has initials RA on candle lifter.
Matching snuffer set. Overall 21cm.
The snuffers are similar in shape to those on Page 38 Fig. 58.
Being a matching set, this combination is very rare.
Brass.
Very rare.                    Date c.1720                    Value £1000

*Fig. 67*

Objects associated with candles. From left to right:

(a) Small candle extinguisher and tray.
Brass.
Uncommon.        Date c.1850        Value £30

(b) Go-to-bed. Inscribed 'Prince Albert's Safety Box 100 Patent Vesta Lights'. The lid acts as the candle socket.
Brass.
Uncommon.        Date c.1850        Value £60

(c) Matchbox holder.
Brass.
Uncommon.        Date c.1850        Value £50

**Fig. 68**

Matchbox with eccentrically operated lid with rasp surface under-
neath for striking.
It is in the form of a pair of candle snuffers. 19cm.
On the base are the letters AFC in logo.
The handles having a small hole also constitute a cigar cutter.
On heavy cast brass C-scroll tray. 24.5cm.
Brass.
Rare.                              Date c.1840              Value £125 the set

**Fig. 69**

Cigar cutter, in the form of a pair of candle snuffers.
Brass. 14.5cm
Rare.                    Date c.1840                    Value £55

**Fig. 70**

Chamberstick with dousing cone or podkin (archaic term).
Old Sheffield Plate.
Pair of Close-plated tapered candle snuffers fit slot in stem. 13cm
Common.            Date c.1800-1820            Value £150

**Fig. 71**

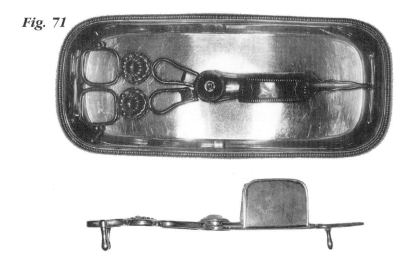

Pair of candle snuffers 18.5cm on matching snuffer tray. 21.5cm.
Both Old Sheffield Plate. Silver mounts on snuffers.
Very rare.　　　　　　　Date c.1800　　　　Value £190 the set

**Fig. 72**

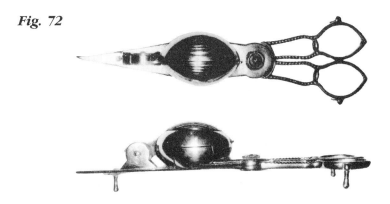

Pair of quality oval snuffers.
Eccentrically operated blade with 'Patent Warranted' on one side
and '1' on the other.
Close-plated steel.  18.5cm
Rare.　　　　　　　Date c.1810　　　　　　Value £140

**Fig. 73**

Two matching pairs of snuffers by Dixon with marks, on tray by Dixon (see below).
It is as rare to find pairs, as it is to find snuffers and trays by the same maker.
Close-plated with silver mounts.  17cm
Rare.                          Date c.1830          Value £100 (2 pairs)

Snuffer tray by James Dixon & Son with marks 88 and 329.
Pewter.  24.5cm                Date c.1830                Value £40

**Fig. 74**

Pair of snuffers with eccentrically operated blade 'Warranted'.
By the handles pivot are the words 'W R Patent'. 19cm.
Steel with close-plated handles with lead-filled silver mounts.
Uncommon.                      Date c.1830-1837            Value £110

**Fig. 75**

Similar to Fig. 74, but on blade 'W R Patent Warranted'.
By the handles pivot is 'Gilbert' with mark.
All close-plated steel. 19.5cm
Uncommon.                     Date c.1830-1837                     Value £110

**Fig. 76**

Pair of snuffers, eccentrically operated blade 'Patent Warranted'.
Additional sprung side blade for emptying similar to Fig. 39.
Steel with silver handles by Emes & Edward Barnard London.
Very rare. 19cm        Date 1819 London                Value £450

**Fig. 77**

Pair of snuffers (missing centre boss).
Close-plated steel with silver handles. George III. 17.5cm
Rare.                         Date 1814 London                        Value £275

**Fig. 78**

Pair of snuffers.
Close-plated steel with silver handles (no marks). 15.5cm
Rare.                         Date 18th cent.                        Value £210

**Fig. 79**

Pair of ornate snuffers by Hutton.
Close-plated with silver mounts.  19.5cm
Uncommon.            Date early 19th cent.            Value £120
On...
Old Sheffield Plate snuffer tray.  25.5cm
Uncommon.                  Date c.1800                  Value £45


**Fig. 80**

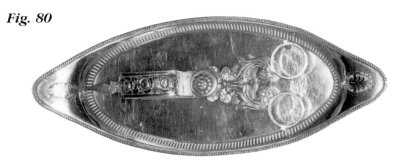

Pair of Portuguese snuffers.
Marks - crowned L and pallet mark.
Silver - Lisbon.  16cm
Uncommon.            Date 1816-1828            Value £140
On...
Old Sheffield Plate snuffer tray.  25cm
Oval fretted.
Uncommon.                  Date c.1800                  Value £50

**Fig. 81**

Pair of wick trimmers with no box.
Silver - no marks.  16.5cm
Rare.                    Date George III c.1790            Value £425
On...
Old Sheffield Plate snuffer tray.  24.5cm
Swivel base - crest lion holding shield.
Rare.                    Date c.1800            Value £125

*Fig. 82*

Pair of snuffers by William Bailey London.
Silver.   16.5cm
Rare.                     Date c.1790                     Value £325
On...
Snuffer tray with feet.   24cm
Silver - I & JW & Co - Waterhouse, Hodson & Co, Sheffield.
Rare.                     Date c.1828                     Value £460

**Fig. 83**

Pair of snuffers by John Buckett, London.
Silver with face on boss.  17cm
Rare.                                    Date c.1771                              Value £450
On...
Snuffer tray with crest.  23.5cm
Silver - Joseph & John Angell, London.
Rare.                                    Date c.1839                              Value £375


**Fig. 84**

Pair of snuffers with eccentrically operated blade.
Silver by Thomas Robinson, London.  19cm
Rare.                                    Date c1823                               Value £500
On...
Snuffer tray - heavy
Silver - William Allen. Third mark London.  25cm
Rare.                                    Date c1803                               Value £450

*Fig. 85*

Pair of snuffers by John Younge & Co, Sheffield.
Silver with crest.  17.5cm
Rare.                    Date c.1800                    Value £400
On...
Snuffer tray by Peter & William Bateman, London.
Silver with crest.
Rare.                    Date c.1810                    Value £325

*Fig. 86*

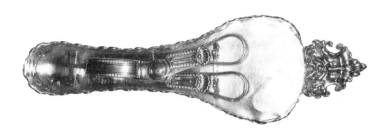

Pair of snuffers with no legs.
Silver by Thomas Robinson, London.
With crest.  13cm
Rare.                    Date c.1821                    Value £325
On...
Snuffer tray – fretted with finger loop under handle with face.
In the tray which has feet there are stands for snuffer.
Silver by JA & IA Joseph and John Angel, London.  23cm
Rare.                    Date c.1834                    Value £600

# Index of makers

## SNUFFERS

### Iron, wrought iron, cast iron and tinned iron
Maker unknown                  Figs. 1, 2, 3, 7, 38, 50

### Steel
| | |
|---|---|
| Bright and Sons | Fig. 29 |
| Brookes | Figs. 6, 10 |
| Cope and Cutler | Figs. 16, 31 |
| Duff (John, Great Pulteney Street, London) | Fig. 28 |
| Hall (John and Co., Manchester) | Fig.15 |
| Hobday (Samuel, Birmingham) | Figs. 17, 19 |
| JAH and Co. | Fig. 52 |
| Lees (Thomas) | Fig. 27 |
| Lund | Fig. 20 |
| Morton | Fig. 23 |
| Rodgers and Sons (Sheffield) | Fig. 26 |
| Rove and Co. | Fig. 11 |
| Tomlinson and Son (Sheffield) | Fig. 53 |
| Willmores (Birmingham) | Fig. 30 |
| Maker unknown | Figs. 4, 5, 8, 9, 18, 21, 22, 33, 34, 35, 48, 51, 74 |

### Nickel-silver
| | |
|---|---|
| Haig and Co. | Fig. 49 |
| Maker unknown | Figs. 44, 45, 46, 47 |

### Bronze
| | |
|---|---|
| Maker unknown | Fig. 37 |

### Brass
| | |
|---|---|
| Maker unknown | Figs. 57, 58, 59, 60, 61, 62, 63, 64, 65, 66, 67, 68, 69 |

### Old Sheffield Plate
| | |
|---|---|
| Maker unknown | Figs. 70, 71 |

## Close-plated silver

| | |
|---|---|
| Armfield (Samuel) | Fig. 32 |
| Cope and Cutler | Fig. 14 |
| Cutler (T., Birmingham) | Fig. 25 |
| Dixon (James and Sons, Sheffield) | Fig. 73 |
| Gilbert | Figs. 24, 75 |
| Hobday (Samuel, Birmingham) | Fig. 13 |
| Hutton (William & Sons, Sheffield) | Fig. 79 |
| Prime (Thomas & Son, Birmingham) | Fig. 41 |
| Shrapnel (Henry Needham Scrope, London) | Fig. 25 |
| Maker unknown | Figs. 12, 36, 39, 40, 42, 43, 72 |

## Silver

| | |
|---|---|
| Bailey (William, London) | Fig. 82 |
| Barnard (Emes and Edward), London) | Fig. 76 |
| Bucket (John, London) | Fig. 83 |
| Robinson (Thomas, London) | Figs. 84, 86 |
| Younge (John and Co., Sheffield) | Fig. 85 |
| Maker unknown | Figs. 77, 78, 80, 81 |

## TRAYS

## Papier-maché

| | |
|---|---|
| Maker unknown | Figs. 55, 56 |

## Toleware

| | |
|---|---|
| Maker unknown | Fig. 54 |

## Iron

| | |
|---|---|
| Maker unknown | Fig. 1 |

## Pewter

| | |
|---|---|
| Broadhead & Atkin (Sheffield) | Fig.38 |
| Dixon (James and Sons, Sheffield) | Fig. 73 |

**Brass**

Maker unknown                                     Figs. 58, 59, 60, 62, 68

**Old Sheffield Plate**

Prime (Thomas and Son,              Fig. 41
     Birmingham)
Maker unknown                            Figs. 71, 79, 80, 81

**Silver**

Allen (William, London)                 Fig. 84
Angel (Joseph and John, London)   Figs. 83, 86
Bateman (Peter and William        Fig. 85
     London)
Waterhouse, Hodson (London)     Fig. 82